Flowers Like Worms

By Kris Bonnell

"I am up here,"

said the flower.

"Come up here!"

3

Pop!

"I am here."

said the worm.

4

"I like worms,"

said the flower.

"Oh, no!

Look!

Here comes a bird!"

said the flower.

"Go!   Go!   Go!"

said the flower.

"I like flowers,"
said the worm.